HALLOWEEN!

ULTIMATE STICKER COLLECTION

HOW TO USE THIS BOOK

Read the captions, then find the sticker that best fits in the space. (Hint: check the sticker labels for clues!)

•

There are lots of eerie extra stickers for creating your own Halloween scenes!

Written and edited by Pamela Afram

Designed by Elena Jarmoskaite and Suzanne Cooper, with assistance from Rhys Thomas and Jon Hall

Jacket designed by Sam Bartlett

First published in Great Britain in 2014
by Dorling Kindersley Limited
One Embassy Gardens, 8 Viaduct Gardens, London, SW11 7BW
A Penguin Random House company

10 9 8 7 6 5 4 3 2
003–318159–Sept/2020

Manufactured by Dorling Kindersley, One Embassy Gardens, 8 Viaduct Gardens, London, SW11 7BW, under licence from the LEGO Group.

Imported into the EEA by Dorling Kindersley Verlag GmbH. Arnulfstr. 124, 80636 Munich, Germany.

A CIP catalogue record for this book is available from the British Library.

ISBN: 978-0-24143-213-6

Printed and bound in China

A WORLD OF IDEAS:
SEE ALL THERE IS TO KNOW
www.dk.com
www.LEGO.com

MONSTER BASH

Who said gruesome beasts don't know how to have fun? This monster's Mega Monster Bash is off to a roaring start and some of his most fearsome friends have arrived to join in the fun.

SOME OF MY DANCE MOVES ARE REALLY FRIGHTENING!

MR. GOOD AND EVIL

This minifigure is in two minds about whether he's enjoying the party. One minute he's dancing and drinking cocktails, the next he's growling at the guests!

EVIL DWARF

The Evil Dwarf isn't exactly a monster, but the others think his terrible temper and grisly appearance are pretty monstrous.

YETI

The party guests rarely understand what the Yeti's saying, but they do know to stay away from its ice-lolly or things could get really hairy!

CRAZY SCIENTIST

This loopy genius likes to experiment on monsters. He's brought a green potion with him, which he says can change ordinary monsters into terrible minifigures!

MINOTAUR

Half-minifigure and half-bull, the fearsome Minotaur rarely attends parties. But he's managed to find a way out of his maze just in time!

THE MONSTER

If there's one thing The Monster does well it's host a party. It's also the perfect place to show off his moves on the dance floor!

ALIEN VILLAINESS

The Alien Villainess doesn't like parties. She's here to study these lifeforms to get information that will help her take over planet Earth.

CYCLOPS

The Cyclops is really excited about the Monster Bash. He can always see eye to eye with this unusual mob!

FRIGHT NIGHT

Look out! As darkness sweeps across the town and a misty fog covers the ground, beware who is lurking in the shadows. These creepy minifigures wreak havoc and terror wherever they go.

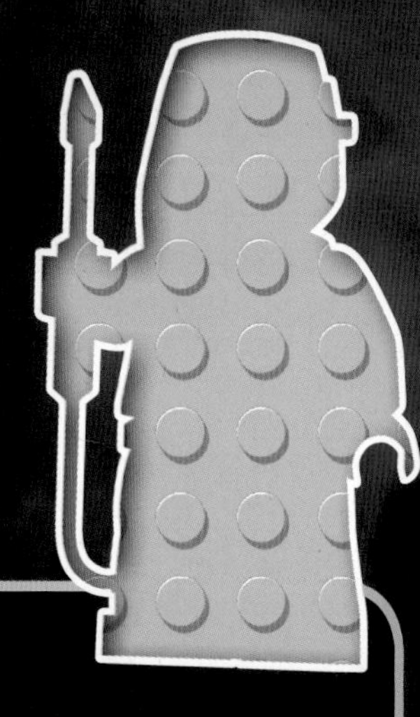

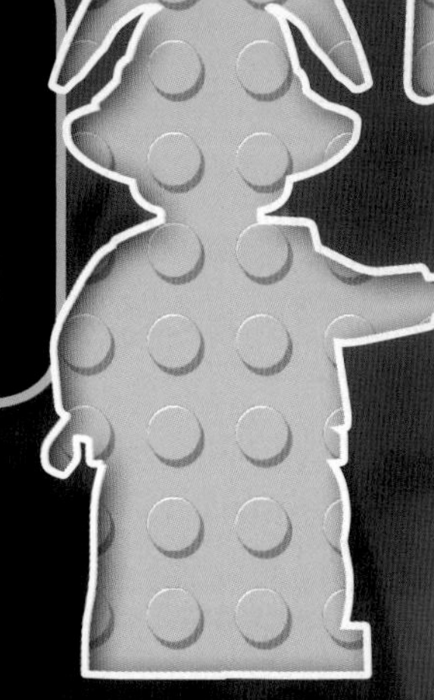

SCARECROW

Nothing rustles the stuffing in this minifigure – he thinks he is the scariest of them all! Unfortunately for him, the bird on his head doesn't agree.

WELDER

The Welder's mask is a startling sight on a dreary night. But ever since an unfortunate welding accident, he can't take it off!

VAMPIRE BAT

As a chief hench-bat for monstrous mobsters, this minifigure tends to hang around in dark nooks and crannies looking for mischief!

HAZMAT GUY

The sight of this minifigure spreads panic – you never know whether he's far from a stream of toxic slime and revolting sludge.

VAMPIRE

This fang-toothed terror likes to take long walks (after sunset, of course!) And he always takes his pet bat with him for company.

BAT

Black clouds of these shrieking bats leave their nests on gloomy nights. Their tiny bodies create eerie shapes in the sky.

GHOST

BOO! This minfigure loves to pop out from behind bins to spook unsuspecting minifigures.

SPOOKY TREE

A creepy forest is the perfect hiding place. This tree is where the Werewolf stashes his bones.

WEREWOLF

Arroooo! Under the light of a full moon the Werewolf changes from a cuddly chew-bone-crazed hound into a terrifying beast!

GRAVE DANGER

The weirdest creatures lurk in this eerie graveyard. And when the sun sets, they crawl out of their hiding places looking for minifigures to scare. BOOOO!

MAKE NO BONES ABOUT IT, THIS PLACE IS REALLY SCARY!

WITCH

The wicked Witch thinks the graveyard is perfect for collecting creepy crawlies for her potions.

SPOOKY SPIRIT

Wooo! This ghost creeps up behind you. But you can often hear it coming because of its clanging chain.

SNAKES

Hiss! Slippery serpents wriggle and slide through the gravestones.

BLACK SKELETON

This skeleton was once a valiant knight. Now he roams the graveyard with his bow and arrow searching for a battle.

ZOMBIE

The Zombie has red eyes from too many late nights. He mindlessly stumbles around the graveyard hunting for dead flesh to eat.

Use your extra stickers
to create your own scene.

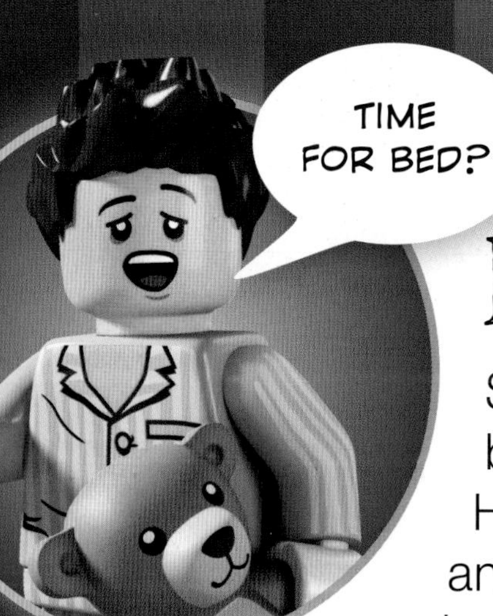

KNIGHTMARE!

Sleepyhead went to bed early as usual but now he's having a terrible nightmare. He dreams of the evil Dragon Wizard and his group of deadly knights, who are concocting a terrible plan…

BASIL THE BAT LORD

Once Basil was a courageous knight, but the Dragon Wizard placed a vile curse on him. Now he might fight in his evil clan.

SLEEPYHEAD

Early nights and late mornings are typical for this minifigure. He and his friend Teddy are always ready for bed.

DRAGON WIZARD

This wicked wizard leads a clan of raging knights who creep into bedrooms and terrify sleeping minifigures!

EVIL KNIGHT

Nothing makes this savage knight happier than a good battle. He'll take up arms for any cause, as long as it's a cruel one.

SKELETON QUEEN

It's easy to spot this frightful skeleton Queen as she creeps up behind you – her creaky old bones make an awful racket!

VLADEK

There's nothing quite so frightening as this barbarous knight racing toward you with his sword of blackest coal.

CHESS QUEEN

The Chess Queen is the most powerful villain in this deadly plot. She can sneak up on you from any direction!

SKELETON DARK KNIGHT

This murderous knight's large axe and creepy red eyes will keep even the most sleepy minifigures up at night.

ALIEN INVASION

Extraterrestrials have landed on Earth with one ghastly mission: To capture as many minifigures as they can and take them back to their own planet for research. There's no time to escape!

CLASSIC ALIEN

The invading aliens don't recognise this alien. He's been on Earth so long, his species is now extinct!

ALIEN CONQUEST FARMER

This burly farmer was working in his field when the aliens landed. They tried to beam him up into their ship, but he managed to fight them off with his pitchfork.

ALIEN DEFENDER

This defence unit soldier has come to Earth's rescue! His vehicle has an anti-UFO laser and missiles that can destroy the mothership!

SPACE ALIEN

After many years on Earth, this Space Alien has heard rumours of an invasion. He's come to see if his distant cousins need help.

ALIEN MOTHERSHIP

Hovering above the cornfields, this spaceship sends instructions to smaller ships down on Earth.

AHAHAH AHAH THERE'S NO ESCAPE, PUNY EARTHLINGS!

ALIEN COMMANDER

The Alien Commander has its own secret plan: To drain the brainpower out of every Earthling to increase its powers!

ALIEN AVENGER

Finally, a cause the Alien Avenger can really get behind! He's been working in a coffee shop just waiting for the perfect invasion!

ALIEN BUGGOID

As if the sight of this bug-like alien, with its armoured skin, wasn't fearsome enough, it's also armed with a powerful sonic handgun.

ALIEN PILOT

Aboard this small alien spacecraft, this bug-eyed creature is scouring Earth for poor minifigures to capture.

WITCHING HOUR

When it's dark and dreary outside, the spooky sorceresses come out of hiding. Wicked witches cook up spells, practise their cackling and fly around doing tricks on their broomsticks.

PUMPKIN

A bright orange pumpkin is a sure sign that witches are abroad.

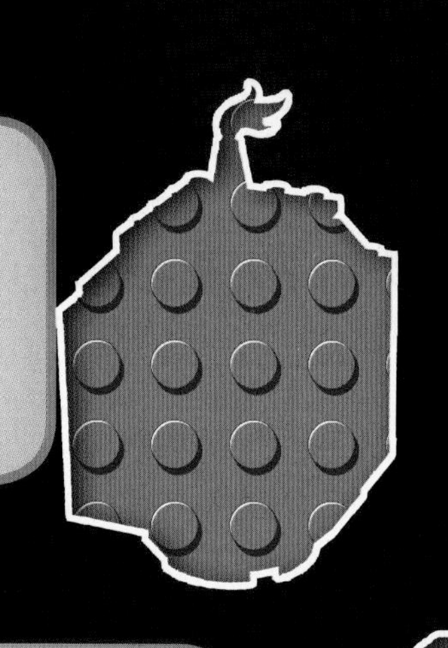

EVIL WITCH

This dark sorceress shoots deadly bolts of lighting at anyone she sees. You know, just because she can!

EVIL WIZARD

A nasty piece of work, this powerful magician uses his magical staff to control his ferocious pet dragon.

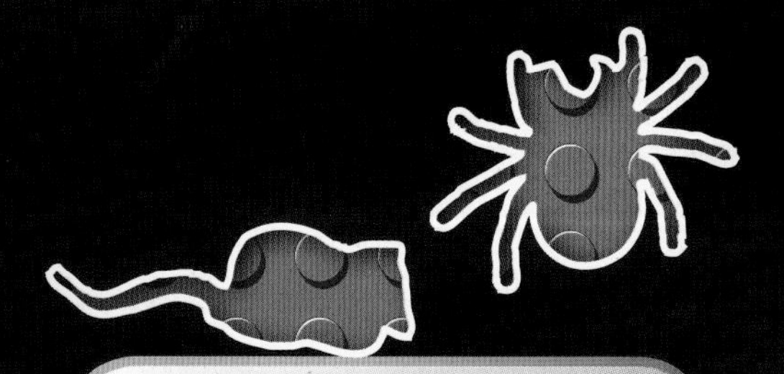

CREEPY CRAWLIES

Mice and spiders collected at midnight are just the thing for potent potions and spooky spells.

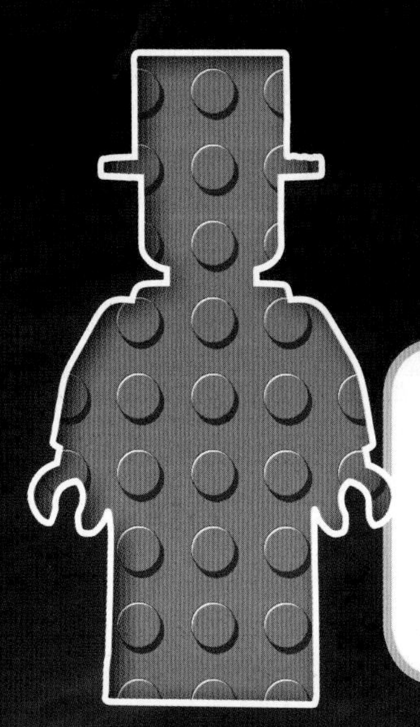

SCARY SKELETON

This terrible skeleton is the Evil Wizard's deadly assistant. He doesn't talk very much, but he rattles an awful lot!

Use your extra stickers
to create your own scene.

ROOAAAAAAR!

SPOOKY CASTLE

Lord Vampyre and his bride have brought six powerful stones together in their eerie castle. They plan to use them to cloak the world in darkness. However, two brave Monster Fighters have arrived to stop this dark plan.

SKELETON

The castle is full of old skeletons. Some are there for decoration, the others help with the housework!

BLACK NET

Jack McHammer's nifty net-launcher is perfect for catching troublesome bats.

BAT MONSTER

This screeching fiend is Lord Vampyre's evil hench-bat. It swoops in to attack anyone who threatens its master!

JACK MCHAMMER

With his armed car and large hammer, courageous monster hunter Jack McHammer is ready to fight!

MOONSTONES

These six magical stones have the power to block out the sun and cast the world into eternal darkness.

GLOWING BRIDE

Lord Vampyre's Bride is truly hideous. She pours a poisonous green potion on anyone who tries to enter the castle.

BAT STATUE

Lord Vampyre likes bats. He has decorated his castle with many diabolical stone statues of them.

DRAMATIC DUEL

Brave Monster Fighter Dr. Rathbone is not afraid! He'll destroy the vile vampire with his handy pistol.

BUILD YOUR OWN MINIFIGURES

What creepy combinations can you dream up? Mix and match the stickers to create your own scary minifigures!

THESE MONSTERS ARE MORE MIXED UP THAN I AM!

CAN YOU MAKE ME EVEN MORE SCARY?

Use the spare body parts to create your own monsters.

PREPARE TO MEET YOUR DOOM!

EVIL ARMY

The Evil Mech is leading a troop of robots set on creating interplantary chaos and destruction. Each robot has been programmed to do one thing: D-E-S-T-R-O-Y!

EVIL MECH

Is the world as you know it coming to a terrifying end? Then the Evil Mech's work is almost done.

WINGED MOSQUITOID

Buzzz! You can hear this green mechanical pest zipping around your ears, but you won't be able to catch it – it moves faster than the eye can see!

RED SIDEKICK

It's time to fight back. This robot is armed with energy blades for battle and a jetpack in case he needs to make a speedy escape.

CLOCKWORK ROBOT

Once just a regular toy, the Clockwork Robot has been turned into a wound-up plaything set on destruction!

EVIL ROBOT
The Evil Robot has brought his biggest, meanest laser gun for the battle. But he's not sure how to use it. Don't tell the Evil Mech!
DARK AZURE SIDEKICK
You need robots to fight robots! This minifigure is part of a team of mechanical warriors who will defend planet Earth till the bitter end!
LADY ROBOT
Where's the party? The Lady Robot thought she was attending a celebration of artificial intelligence, not a battle.
WE'LL FIGHT UNTIL THE LAST BRICK FALLS!
CLS-89
ERADICATOR MECH
Billy Starbeam can rely on his robot sidekicks and this giant robot to fight off the evil army!
BILLY STARBEAM
Armed with a laser gun, there's only one minifigure who can put an end to the Evil Mech's plans: Billy Starbeam. The best shot in the galaxy!

MAYBE I'LL DISCOVER A NEW SPECIES!

SWAMP MONSTERS

The LEGO® swamp is home to revolting bog weed, creepy crawlies and a whole host of horrible beasts lurking in the shadows. BEWARE!

ON GUARD

This minifigure is the ever-watchful guardian of the swamp. No minifigure can get past his unblinking eye!

PORTAL EMPEROR

This warrior doesn't like visitors. He uses his golden trident to prod anyone who decides to take a paddle.

LIZARD MAN

Legend has it that a giant reptile lurks in the bog, but it is just the Lizard Man who comes here sometimes for a swim.

MEDUSA

Watch out! One look in this minifigure's eyes and you will be turned into stone forever!

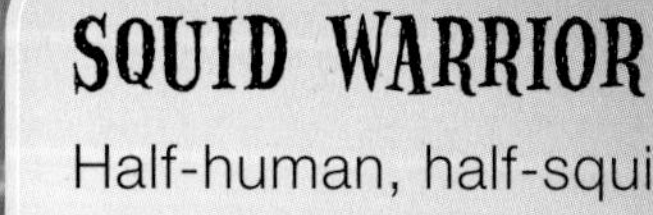

SQUID WARRIOR

Half-human, half-squid, this warrior lives at the bottom of the swamp—he guards the entrance to a long-forgotten land.

Use your extra stickers
to create your own scene.

FANCY DRESS

Lord Vampyre keeps his precious top hat in this chest. He likes to wear it whenever there's an eclipse.

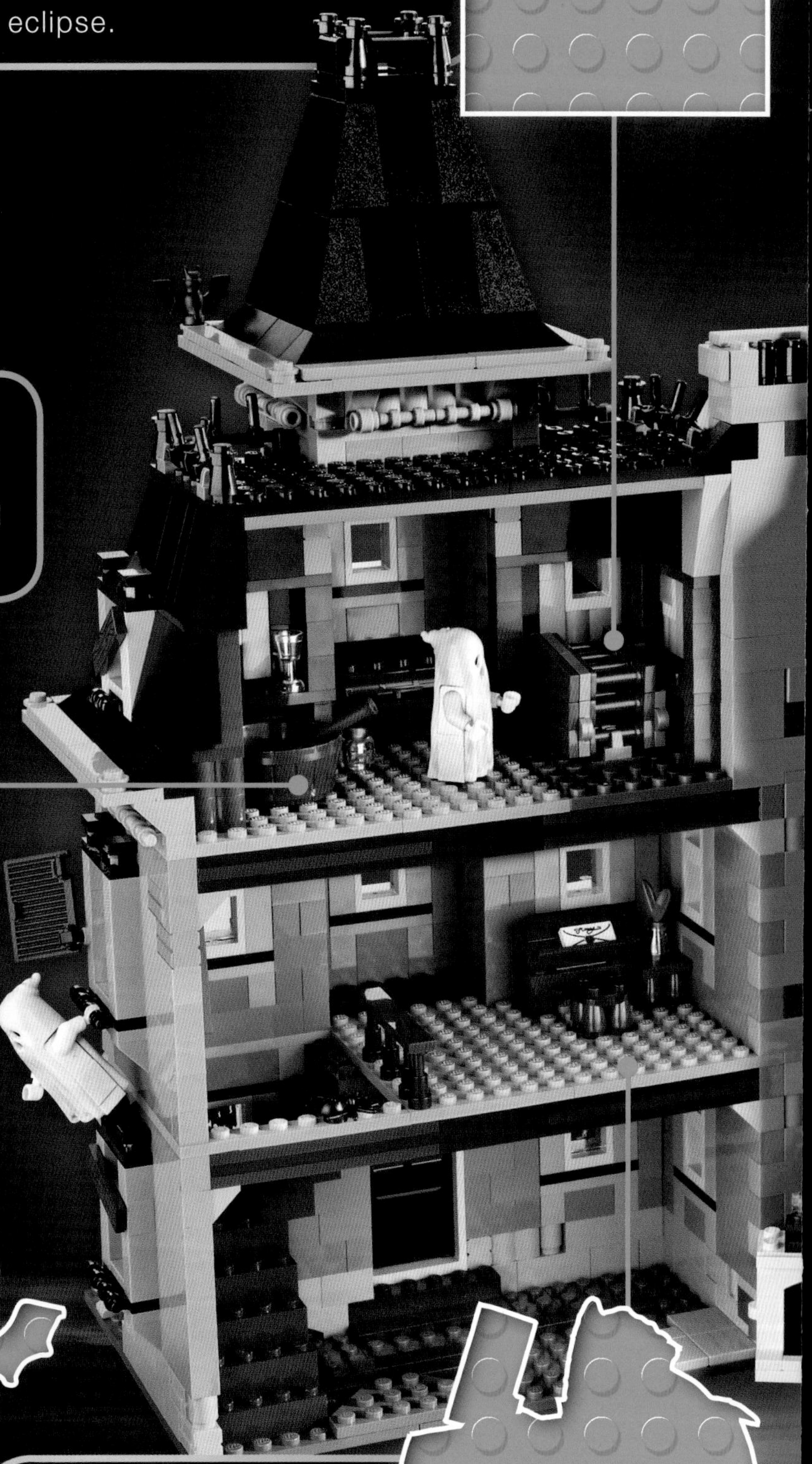

HORRID HOME

Beware! Unfortunate minifigures who enter this deadly household never return!

AWFUL BREW

A large wooden bowl makes a perfect cauldron for mixing a potion made with bones.

BLACK BATS

Screeching, flapping bats hang around the house. They make very noisy pets!

POISON LETTER

Lord Vampyre uses his office to write poison pen letters to his enemies.

HAUNTED HOUSE

Deep in a dark forest is a strange old house, long abandoned by its human inhabitants. Ghosts roam the halls and peculiar characters lurk inside... Enter at your peril!

RECORD PLAYER

The only form of entertainment in this hellish abode is an old record player that plays eerie tunes.

SNAKE POTION

You won't find anything tasty in the kitchen – just the Zombie Chef's slithering snake stew!

GHOSTS

This ghoulish trio are responsible for the eerie sounds echoing through the halls. And they don't like uninvited guests! Wooooo!

TOMB RAIDERS

Archaeologist Professor Archibald Hale and his team disturbed an ancient tomb while on an important excavation for his museum. Now the tomb's unearthly guardians are free to roam the land, terrifying anyone who crosses their path!

PHARAOH ENOUGH!

ARCHIBALD HALE

Professor Hale is determined not to let Amset-Ra escape. He's a deadly sorcerer who will turn everyone into scorpions!

SCORPION

When the tomb was opened, a swarm of these poisonous pests came scuttling out!

FLYING MUMMY

The Flying Mummy protects Amset-Ra's treasure. It will attack anyone who tries to harm its master! Its falcon headress gives it extra-special powers.

HELENA SKVALLING

Helena is an adventurer who shows no fear! She laughs at the sight of stinging scorpions and ghastly mummies!

PHARAOH

The Pharaoh plans to take over this strange kingdom. And when he does, he will use his magical golden staff to make big changes. Where are all the pyramids anyway?

EGYPTIAN QUEEN

Now the Egyptian Queen has been released from the tomb she can take her pet snake to the vet – it has been a little hiss-terical.

MUMMY

The Mummy thinks curses are really funny. Don't be surprised if you find beetles in your sandwich or lizards in your bed.

AMSET-RA

Evil sorcerer Amset-Ra was buried in the tomb a very, very long time ago. Now his peaceful slumber has been disturbed, he's rather grumpy.

ANUBIS GUARD

This ferocious protector was once a stone statue, but it came to life when its tomb was disturbed.

ZOMBIE ZONE

A full moon is overhead and the streets are deathly quiet. But you'd better stay inside and pull the covers over your head – there are zombies on the loose!

ZOMBIE GROOM

For this newlywed, nothing beats the perfection of his hideous bride, except perhaps delicious minifigure bones.

TERROR TIME

Just before three in the morning the still night air is filled with the unsettling cries of the living dead.

SKELETON HORSE

There's no horsing around with this unearthly beast. It will bite any hand that tries to feed it!

ZOMBIE BRIDE

There's just one thing on this beastly bride's mind: Who can she have for breakfast?

ZOMBIE COFFIN CAR

Fiery jets propel this zombie chauffeur's mobile coffin at hellish speed. He can't stand being late for funerals!

Use your extra stickers
to create your own scene.

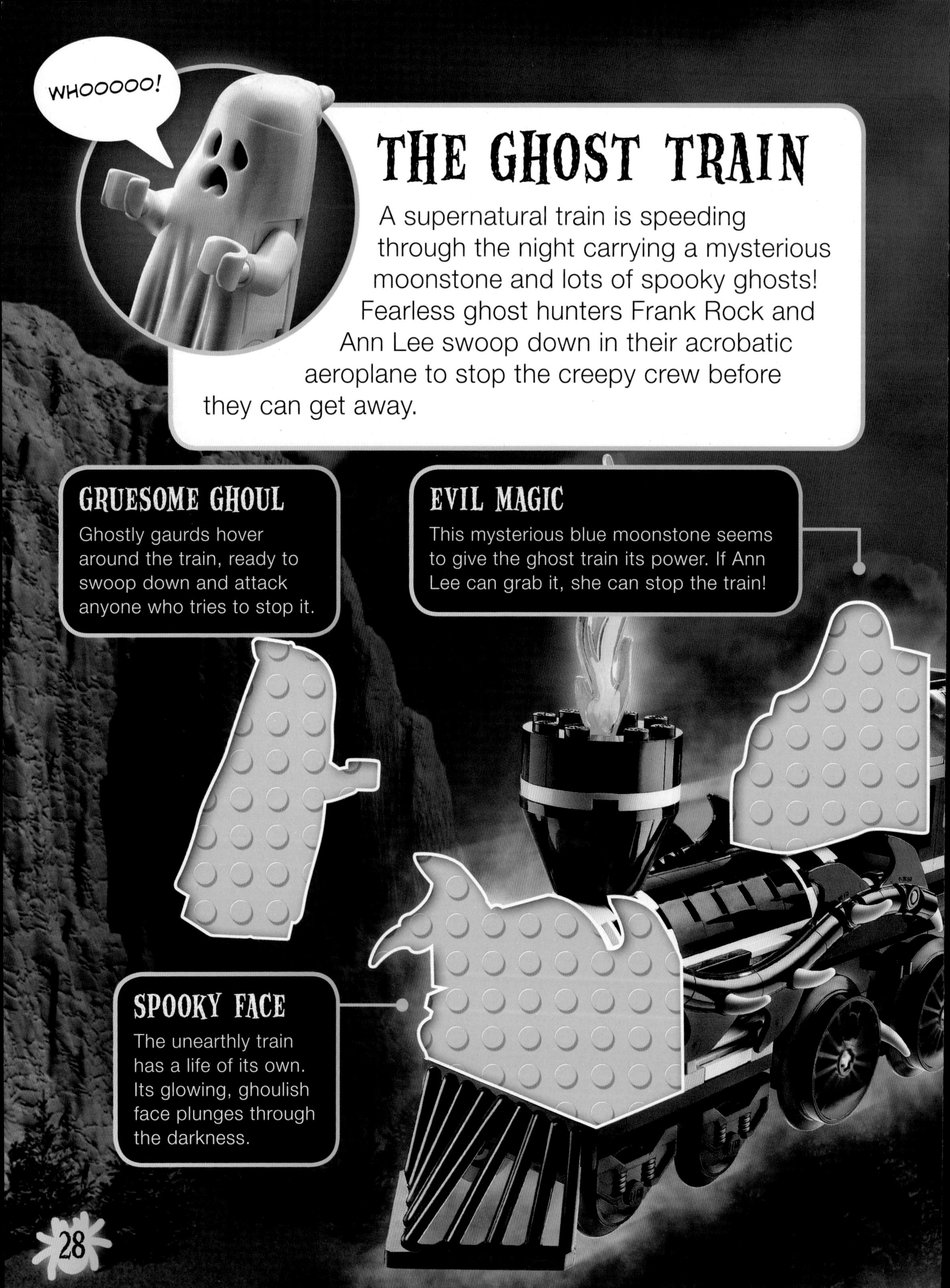

THE GHOST TRAIN

A supernatural train is speeding through the night carrying a mysterious moonstone and lots of spooky ghosts! Fearless ghost hunters Frank Rock and Ann Lee swoop down in their acrobatic aeroplane to stop the creepy crew before they can get away.

GRUESOME GHOUL

Ghostly gaurds hover around the train, ready to swoop down and attack anyone who tries to stop it.

EVIL MAGIC

This mysterious blue moonstone seems to give the ghost train its power. If Ann Lee can grab it, she can stop the train!

SPOOKY FACE

The unearthly train has a life of its own. Its glowing, ghoulish face plunges through the darkness.

ANN LEE

This Monster Fighter should not be messed with! She's a whiz with a bow and arrow and she really hates ghosts!

FRANK ROCK

Nothing gets past Frank. He's a skilled pilot with a pistol filled with anti-ghost serum and he's not afraid to use it!

RIB CAGE

Captured enemies wind up in the prison cell, caged in by the bones of unfortunate minifigures.

FANGS

Covered in sharp fangs and shrouded in a toxic green mist, the spine-chilling train is not of this Earth.

GHOST DRIVER

The ghastly ghoul driving this train glows bright green when it's really angry – like when Monster Fighters try to stop its train.

EVIL SCIENCE

The Crazy Scientist is busy in his sinister laboratory creating a horrible creature. It's only a matter of time until this mad genius succeeds in his grisly experiment. Mwahahaha!

THE CRAZY SCIENTIST

The Crazy Scientist's glowing green potion could finally be the breakthough he needs to bring his monster to life!

THE MUMMY

This grumpy monster hopes the Crazy Scientist can brew him a potion to send him back to sleep.

THE WEREWOLF

Like the Mummy, The Werewolf wants the scientist's help. He longs to be just an ordinary minifigure again.

SCARY SPIDER

This spider crawled into the scientist's special potion. Now it has doubled in size and it's glowing bright green.

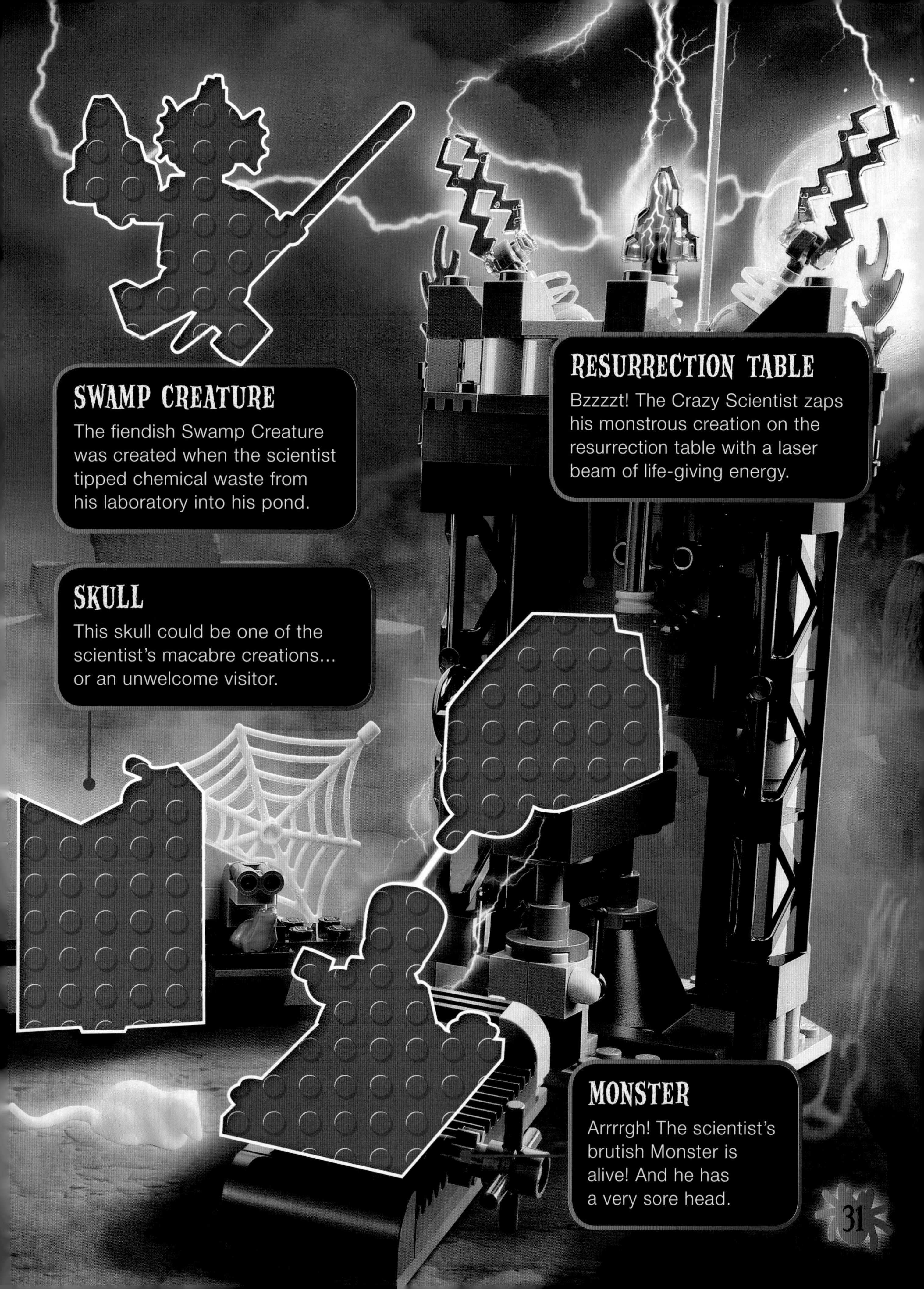

SWAMP CREATURE

The fiendish Swamp Creature was created when the scientist tipped chemical waste from his laboratory into his pond.

RESURRECTION TABLE

Bzzzzt! The Crazy Scientist zaps his monstrous creation on the resurrection table with a laser beam of life-giving energy.

SKULL

This skull could be one of the scientist's macabre creations... or an unwelcome visitor.

MONSTER

Arrrrgh! The scientist's brutish Monster is alive! And he has a very sore head.

DON'T WORRY, YOU WON'T FEEL A THING...

DEADLY DAMSEL

Lord Vampyre's Bride has perfected the art of concocting deadly potions. Take one sip of her tonic and you'll be turned into a zombie or a gruesome bat monster! Hee! hee! hee!

VAMPYRE'S BRIDE

Can you hear an evil chuckle or a delighted cackle? That's probably Lord Vampyre's Bride happily making another brew.

BONES

The last minifigure to cross this beastly bride is now a key ingredient in her evil elixirs.

MANBAT

Once, this minifigure was an ordinary bat. After succumbing to one of the bride's spells, he's now a fearsome beast!

ZOMBIE CHEF

This master chef takes tips from his mistress – maybe he'll add some dusty old bones to his slimy snake stew!

BAD SERVICE

Vampyre's Bride's faithful butler serves her toxic potions to oblivious guests, under the guise of hospitality.

Mr Good and Evil
Minotaur
Monster
Resurrection
Table
Yet
On Guard
The Mummy
© 2020 LEGO

Cyclops
Portal Emperor
Lizard Man
Skull
The Werewolf
The Crazy Scientist
© 2020 LEGO

Medusa
Crazy Scientist
Swamp Creature
Alien Villainess
Evil Dwarf
Scary Spider
The Monster
Squid Warrior
© 2020 LEGO

Mummy
Pharaoh
Spooky Spirit
Moonstones
Anubis Guard
Alien Buggoid
Jack McHammer
Bat Statue
Alien Defender
Black Skeleton
© 2020 LEGO

Classic Alien
Helena Skvalling
Bat Monster
Alien Commander
Alien Conquest Farmer
Skeleton
Zombie
Black Net
Scorpion
Flying Mummy
Snakes
© 2020 LEGO

Archibald Hale
© 2020 LEGO
Amset-Ra
Egyptian Queen
Glowing Bride
Space Alien
Witch
Alien Avenger
Dramatic Duel
Alien Pilot

Evil Knight
Bat
© 2020 LEGO
© 2020 LEGO
© 2020 LEGO
© 2020 LEGO
© 2020 LEGO
Red Sidekick
© 2020 LEGO
© 2020 LEGO
© 2020 LEGO
© 2020 LEGO
© 2020 LEGO
© 2020 LEGO
Werewolf
Zombie Bride
Skeleton Horse
Ghost
© 2020 LEGO
© 2020 LEGO
© 2020 LEGO
© 2020 LEGO
© 2020 LEGO
Hazmat Guy
© 2020 LEGO
© 2020 LEGO
Evil Mech
© 2020 LEGO
© 2020 LEGO
© 2020 LEGO
© 2020 LEGO
© 2020 LEGO
© 2020 LEGO
Welder
Dragon Wizard

Chess Queen
Vladek
Winged Mosquitoid
Billy Starbeam
Vampire
Clockwork Robot
Sleepyhead
Basil the Bat Lord
Evil Robot
© 2020 LEGO

Lady Robot
Skeleton Dark Knight
Scarecrow
Dark Azure Sidekick
Zombie Coffin Car
Zombie Groom
Vampire Bat
Skeleton Queen
Terror Time
© 2020 LEGO

Creepy
Crawlies
Frank Rock
Rib Cage
Snake Potion
Spooky
Face
Bad
Service
Fancy Dress
Manbat
Evil
Witch

Bones
Fangs
Black Bats
Zombie Chef
Evil Wizard
Evil Magic
Poison Letter
Record Player
Gruesome Ghoul
© 2020 LEGO

Awful Brew
Horrid Home
Scary Skeleton
Vampyre's Bride
Ghosts
Pumpkin
Ghost Driver
Ann Lee
© 2020 LEGO

EXTRA STICKERS

EXTRA STICKERS

EXTRA STICKERS

EXTRA STICKERS

EXTRA STICKERS

EXTRA STICKERS

EXTRA STICKERS

EXTRA STICKERS